The Power of Kindness Activity Book

By **Ruth Maille**
Art by **Pencil Master Studio**

ISBNs
hardcover 978-1-955299-01-5
paperback 978-1-955299-02-2
e-book 978-1-955299-00-8

This book belongs to

_____

_____

_____

Color the page

Spot the (10) differences

Circles all around

Find and color in all the items that are circles.

Cookie

Clock

Frame

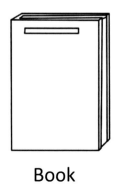

Book

Lamp

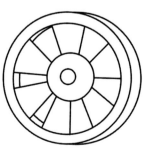

Wheel

Kindness is..

Find the Hidden Kindness words below.

P	L	V	W	S	A	V	I	N	G	T	Z	M	A	Q	D	V	F	S	X
F	K	X	U	G	T	U	H	Y	C	E	P	X	Q	X	C	O	N	R	C
Y	V	C	C	L	G	F	J	B	K	N	R	W	D	G	O	V	Z	E	B
W	D	N	Y	A	A	Y	E	C	J	D	Q	R	Z	U	O	G	D	A	D
P	H	M	G	Q	T	C	A	P	L	E	S	M	W	E	K	P	J	D	Y
B	D	I	W	X	J	T	M	R	I	R	Z	I	G	E	I	X	C	I	T
A	M	C	S	Q	J	E	Z	Y	P	L	E	O	N	X	N	I	W	N	E
B	B	P	K	P	A	Q	W	J	T	O	D	N	P	G	G	I	F	G	C
Y	U	H	T	G	E	A	P	J	B	V	O	G	Q	D	I	D	F	D	O
S	L	K	J	O	E	R	W	O	I	I	N	T	O	P	E	N	I	N	G
I	X	N	U	X	T	R	I	Q	O	N	A	T	F	F	W	O	G	B	V
T	P	P	Y	S	T	L	C	N	I	G	T	J	U	U	M	C	D	R	H
T	Q	L	Z	D	H	H	R	A	G	C	I	W	N	A	U	X	M	E	G
I	J	A	S	N	I	A	T	Y	L	A	N	Q	M	E	W	N	J	S	T
N	K	Y	U	K	F	Y	R	H	O	R	G	B	M	J	U	T	U	C	S
G	T	I	C	Q	M	D	A	I	D	E	Q	G	V	B	D	M	M	U	N
L	Z	N	E	B	E	J	V	W	N	L	T	L	I	N	G	F	B	E	H
E	X	G	L	I	Y	N	H	M	H	G	S	X	Y	K	N	D	N	L	C
M	O	J	W	X	Z	J	R	G	S	J	Y	I	Y	L	D	D	W	V	X
P	P	H	X	H	W	Q	V	Y	W	J	K	V	U	U	R	K	P	I	W

tender loving care	donating	sharing	opening
whispering	reading	cooking	singing	playing
rescue	saving	babysitiing	fun

6

Color the page

Find a Way

Help Dominic get to Sawyer so that he can share his cookie.

Name: _____ # Being Kind is.. Date: _____

Unscramble the words below.

1.   DIAERNG TO UYRO STRSIE _____

2.   DAYDD YNIGLAP A REAC ARC MGEA_____

3.   VIGNIG TO ESRHOT _____

4.   GNKAIS ESOMNOE FI ETHY RAE KO _____

5.   SNAGHRI A KCSAN _____

6.   ENSGNIILT OT A DENFIR _____

7.   IGKTNA AERC OF A ETP _____

8.   GINELCNA UP YRUO YOST _____

9.   YIANSG ELESPA DAN TAKHN YUO_____

10. OHGNIWS YRUO ARTPIPNCEAIO_____

11. NBEIG KNDI OT ROUEFYLS_____

12. SIEGDNN A RCDA TO YAS HI_____

13. IGVING A HUG_____

14. NELTGTI SEOEONM EELS EB FTRSI_____

15. EGINB TALRGEFU_____

9

Color the page

How many Orbits can you find?

I found _____ Orbit's

Color-code

Use the color code to color Dominic.

A -Red   B -Yellow   C -Black   D -Blue   E -Purple   F -Tan

Spot the (10) differences

Complete & Color

Complete the other half of the picture and color the whole picture.

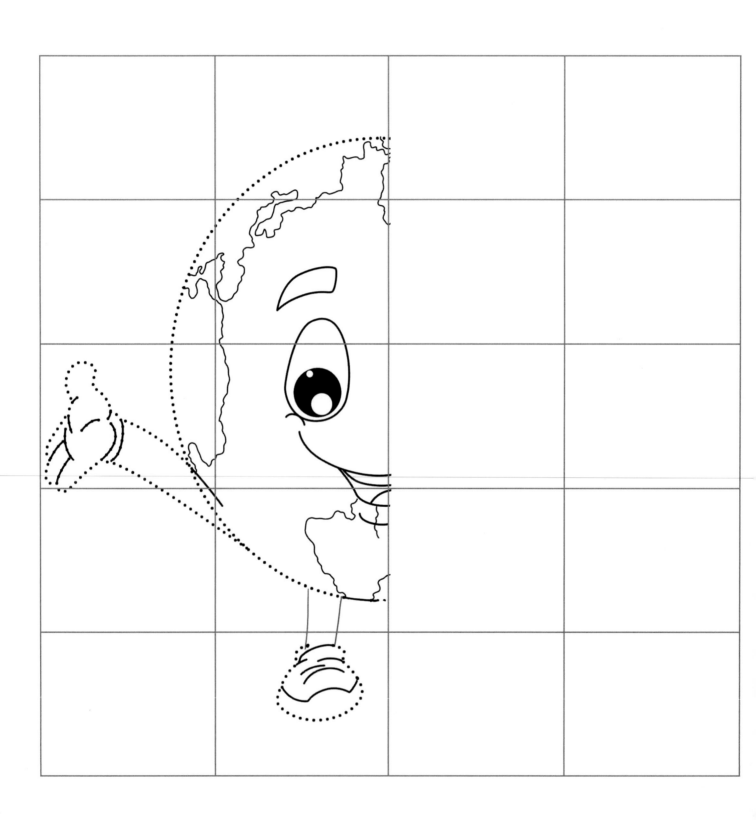

Kindness Matters

Complete the crossword puzzle below.

Across
1. strong intrest on or liking for something
2. to divine and give out to others while keeping a portion for oneself.
4. identification with or sharing of another's feelings, situation, or attitudes.
5. to give in order to help a charity or other group.
7. making sound or noise.

Down
1. wothout company; alone.
3. feeling thankful or showing thanks for kindness or something pleasing
6. gentle or pleasant

Squares all around

Find and color in all the items that are squares.

Pizza

Milk box

Frame

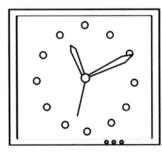

Wall clock

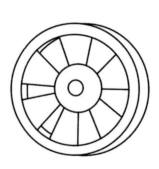

Wheel

Lamp

Connect the Dots

Rectangles all around

Find and color in all the items that are rectangles.

Door

Cupboard

Book

Frame

Lamp

Television

18

How many Orbits can you find?

I found _____ Orbit's

Decode the message

A¹ B² C³ D⁴ E⁵ F⁶ G⁷ H⁸

I⁹ J¹⁰ K¹¹ L¹² M¹³ N¹⁴ O¹⁵ P¹⁶

Q¹⁷ R¹⁸ S¹⁹ T²⁰ U²¹ V²² W²³ X²⁴

Y²⁵ Z²⁶

__ __ __ __ __ __ __ __ is a
11   9   14   4   14   5   19   19

__ __ __ __   __ __ __ __ __ __ __ __
7   9   1   3   5   22   5   18   25   15   14   5

__ __ __   __ __ __ __ __ __   __ __
3   1   14   1   6   6   15   18   4   20   15

__ __ __ __ .
7   9   22   5

Triangles all around

Find and color in all the items that are triangles.

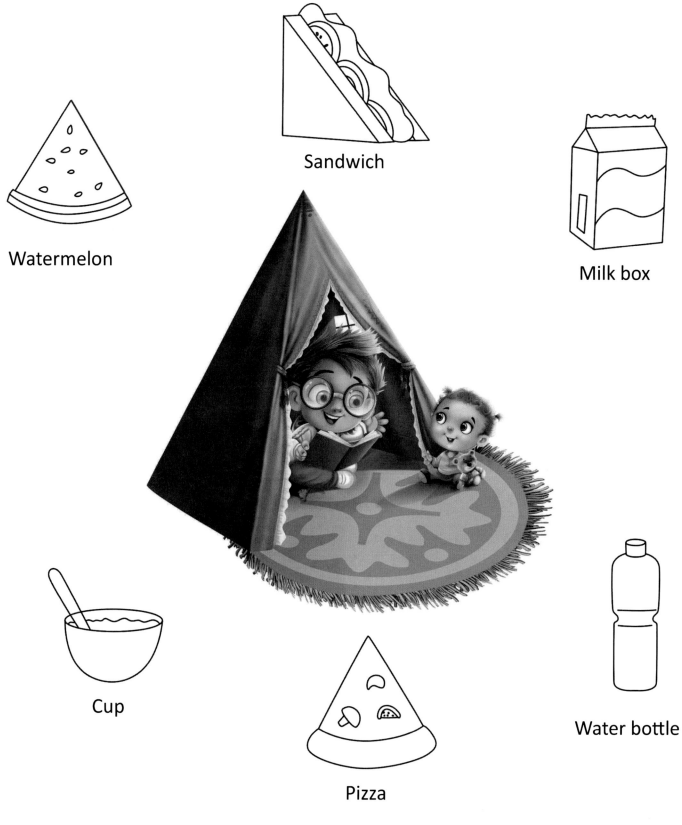

Sandwich

Watermelon

Milk box

Cup

Pizza

Water bottle

Color the page

Spot the (10) differences

Complete & Color

Connect the dots to complete the picture and color it.

Same and Different

Circle the objects that is different in each set.

Color-code

Use the color-code to color the picture.

A -Purple   B -Yellow   C -Blue   D -Red

Color the page

Decode the message

A ^{1} B ^{2} C ^{3} D ^{4} E ^{5} F ^{6} G ^{7} H ^{8}

I ^{9} J ^{10} K ^{11} L ^{12} M ^{13} N ^{14} O ^{15} P ^{16}

Q ^{17} R ^{18} S ^{19} T ^{20} U ^{21} V ^{22} W ^{23} X ^{24}

Y ^{25} Z ^{26}

___ ___ ___   ___ ___ ___ ___   ___ ___ ___ ___
15 14 5   11 9 14 4   23 15 18 4

___ ___ ___   ___ ___ ___ ___ ___ ___
3 1 14   3 8 1 14 7 5

___ ___ ___ ___ ___ ___ 's   ___ ___ ___ .
1 14 25 15 14 5   4 1 25

Connect the dots

Use the Color-key

Use the color-key to color the picture.

A -Red   B -Tan   C -Green   D -Blue   E -Purple   F -Brown

Big and Small

Circle the animals or images that are big and tick (√) the smaller ones.

Color the page

Spot the (10) differences

Decode the message

| A¹ | B² | C³ | D⁴ | E⁵ | F⁶ | G⁷ | H⁸ |

Letter grid:

A_1 B_2 C_3 D_4 E_5 F_6 G_7 H_8

I_9 J_{10} K_{11} L_{12} M_{13} N_{14} O_{15} P_{16}

Q_{17} R_{18} S_{19} T_{20} U_{21} V_{22} W_{23} X_{24}

Y_{25} Z_{26}

No _A_ _C_ _T_ of _K_ _I_ _N_ _D_ _N_ _E_ _S_ _S_ ,
   1 3 20   11 9 14 4 14 5 19 19

_N_ _O_ _M_ _A_ _T_ _T_ _E_ _R_ _H_ _O_ _W_
14 15 13 1 20 20 5 18 8 15 23

_S_ _M_ _A_ _L_ _L_ , is _E_ _V_ _E_ _R_
19 13 1 12 12   5 22 5 18

_W_ _A_ _S_ _T_ _E_ _D_ .
23 1 19 20 5 4

Color the page

Kindness Matters

Complete the crossword puzzle below.

Across

1. in a start of being thrilled
3. to pick one or more from a group.
5. a particular task or duty done out of strong belief.
6. full of kindness; friendly.
7. the fact or condition of being glad.

Down

2. the particular method or way of doing or performing something.
4. the act of talking in and letting out air.
8. to call out loudly

Write a letter to Orbit and send it via email to ruthmaille@gmail.com
Orbit will be sure to get and even reply

Dear Orbit,

_____

_____

_____

_____

_____

_____

_____

_____

_____

_____

_____

_____

_____

Kindness Matters
and I can make a difference!

My Name is: _____

My big reward is: _____

Below are various Acts of Kindness. See how many you can accomplish in one month. The tree of hearts gives you a chance to choose your Act of Kindness and a small reward. Finish the entire chart and earn A BIG REWARD.

Answers

Page 3.

Page 5.

Page 7.

Page 8.
1. reading to your sister 2. Daddy playing a race car game 3. giving to others 4. asking someone if they are ok 5. sharing a snack 6. listening to a friend 7. taking care of a pet 8. cleaning up your toys 9. saying please and thank you 10. Showing your appreciation 11. being kind to yourself 12. sending a card to say hi 13. giving a hug 14. letting someone else be first 15. being grateful

Page 10.
6
Page 11.

Page 14.
1. love 1. lonely 2. sharing 3. grateful 4. empathy 5. donate 6. sweet 7. quiet
Page 18.
6
Page 19.
Kindness is a gift everyone can afford to give.
Page 22.

Page 27.
One kind word can change anyone's day.
Page 33.
No act of kindness, no matter how small, is ever wasted.
Page 32.

Page 35.
1. excited 2. technique 3. choose 4. breath 5. mission 6. warm 7. happiness 8. shout

Other books by Ruth Maille

The Power of Kindness
Through the Eyes of Children
Available in E-Book, Paperback and Hardcover.

"The Power of Kindness: Through the Eyes of Children, explores the many forms of kindness as seen through the eyes of a group of kindergarten children. Using Orbit, a character in the shape of planet Earth as the leader, the children in a kindergarten class are asked to share their ideas on "What is kindness?" The answers are simple, but also very profound. To see things through the eyes of children is empowering. The illustrations are bright and colorful and certainly add to the story."

"The many answers provided by children exemplify the concept that kindness is a simple act, sometimes just a word, that can make another person's day a little brighter. The question/answer approach also opens the door to allowing readers to contribute some of their ideas and there's even a page at the end for young readers to write or draw their own definition of kindness. Beautifully told and presented."

Review By Emily-Jane Hills Orford for Readers' Favorite

The Power of Positivity
The ABC's of Pandemic
Available in E-Book, Paperback and Hardcover.
Also Available in Spanish

This beautifully illustrated book combines the alphabet letters with encouraging words to help children focus on positive experiences during the 2020 pandemic. Reading this book with your child will help them see the rays of sunshine that can be found in even the gloomiest circumstances. This book will become a symbol of the current decade that can be handed down through generations.

Also available are: Coloring book and Activity Book.

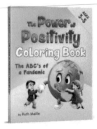
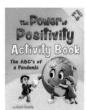

Coloring pages and activity pages are designed to encourage kindness, love, and positivity. Have fun helping Orbit spread kindness while traveling through a maze of twists and turns. Seek and find the hidden Teddy Bears. Discover the many ways to show love through challenging word search and follow clues to decode, just like a scientist. Don't forget to make your very own time capsule so one day you can look back and remember the joyous moments of this pandemic.

Sign up to be notified about future books released at
www.ruthmaille-author.com

More ways to connect with the Author

✉ ruthmaille@gmail.com

f @RuthAnnSimonelliMailleauthor

📷 @ruth.maille

Bristol Rhode Island USA +1-401-556-0084

Made in the USA
Middletown, DE
07 October 2021

49759816R00024